D1430900

Traditional Chinese Therapeutic Exercises and Techniques

14-SERIES
SINEW-TRANSFORMING
EXERCISES

Compiled by: Chang Weizhen
Translated by: Hong Yunxi

FOREIGN LANGUAGES PRESS   BEIJING

First Edition   1988

ISBN 0-8351-2311-1
ISBN 7-119-00636-3

Copyright 1988 by Foreign Languages Press,
Beijing, China

Published by Foreign Languages Press
24 Baiwanzhuang Road, Beijing, China

Distributed by China International Book Trading Corporation
(Guoji Shudian), P.O. Box 399, Beijing, China

Printed in the People's Republic of China

Contents

On the Historical Origins of the Sinew-Transforming Exercises

—In Lieu of a Preface

By Professor Chang Renxia

The "Sinew-Transforming Exercises"[1] are just one of the many forms of exercise constituting the traditional Chinese art today known as Qi Gong[2] (literally breath exercises). Qi Gong originated from the Taoist and medicinal traditions of ancient China. Tradition ascribes its beginnings to the Yellow Emperor,[3] one of the legendary great ancestors of the Chinese nation, who is believed to have lived between 2698 and 2598 B.C. The only book attributed to him that has been handed down to the present is the *Yellow Emperor's Classics of Internal Medicine*,[4] which was compiled almost certainly between the third and first centuries B.C.

"The *Classics of Internal Medicine* comprises eighteen volumes," states the "Annals of Art" in the *History of the Han Dynasty*,[5] which was edited by the celebrated historian Ban Gu[6] (A.D. 32-92). Huangfu Mi[7] (A.D. 215-282), a noted medical scientist of the Jin Dynasty, said in his *ABC of Acupuncture and Moxibustion*[8]: "Today there exists the 'Classic of Needling'[9] and 'Plain Questions,'[10] each comprising nine volumes, which

1

combine to form the eighteen-volume *Classics of Internal Medicine*." An exegesis of the *Classics of Internal Medicine* was written by Yang Shangshan[11] of the Sui Dynasty (581-618) under the title of "Beginnings of Substance."[12] Wang Bing[13] of the Tang Dynasty (618-907) wrote the earliest extant commentary on "Plain Questions" re-editing it in eighteen volumes by combining "Plain Questions" with "The Vital Axis,"[14] another name for the "Nine Mysterious Instruments,"[15] which appeared as the title of the second half of the *Classics of Internal Medicine* in the "Annals of Literature," *History of the Sui Dynasty*.[16]

However the present complete text of "Plain Questions" is not the original since it seems the complete version of the *Classics of Internal Medicine* was lost in the Southern Song, Kin or Yuan dynasties (A.D. 1115-1368). Towards the end of the last century, fortunately, Yang Xingwu[17] of the late Qing Dynasty returned from Japan with a hand-copied volume of a Tang Dynasty edition of the *Beginnings of Substance*. The book contains references indicating the long existence of certain so-called "Marrow-Transforming Exercises,"[18] which have close ties with the Sinew-Transforming Exercises. It is also noted in the book:

"Dao Yin[19] moving exercises—relaxed movement of the body combined with regulation of the mind and respiration, include a variety of forms imitating animal movements, such as the Bear Twisting His Neck, the Stretching Bird and the Frolics of Five Animals.[20] These can in the short term cure all kinds of diseases and in the long term ensure a long and healthy life (free from senile decline)." (See *Ishin Ho*,[21] or *Prescrip-*

tions of Internal Medicine, an ancient Japanese book, Volume 27, where Yang Shangshan's exegesis is quoted.)

According to *Classics of Internal Medicine*, "All diseases are latent in the condition of the *qi*, or vital energy." It is said that if one can keep *yin* and *yang*, the two opposite vital properties that permeate the whole body, in harmonious proportion, accordingly nourishing one's blood and vital energy, then one can ward off disease, extend one's years and ensure a long and healthy life free from senile decline. The beneficial effects of Qi Gong on health are therefore well established.

Qi Gong exercises of this tradition may be divided into the "quiet," which usually consist of conscious breathing movement to "exhale the stale and take in the fresh," and the "active," which consist of the art of limb movement, such as the above-mentioned Frolics of the Five Animals. These exercises combining body movement with mental regulation are considered a necessary means to promoting the free function of the vital energy and blood circulation. Perform such exercises every day, and one's health is ensured. These are the ways the ancients preserved their health, methods which have been passed down to us through Taoist preachings and medical texts. In fact, ancient healing arts may well have had their origin in sorcery, a fact which was also noted by Confucianists. "A man without perseverance cannot be a wizard-doctor," said Confucius (551-479 B.C.). Mencius, his great disciple, was often quoted as saying, "I am skillful in nourishing my all-pervading energy," which may well refer to the

3

practice of a form of Qi Gong. Another tradition passed down by Taoists is contained in the *Canon of Great Void*,[22] an ancient Taoist work still extant, which advocates the practice of lower abdominal respiration—what is known as "moving the *qi* down to the Dantian"[23] (a point below the navel), and complete spiritual freedom without desires and ambitions. It has the following lines in verse:

> *Toughen my sinews, harden my bones,*
> *Make my blood flow freely,*
> *I will then be young forever*
> *In touch with the realm of gods.*

According to Taoist preachings, the taking of pellets and drugs is a form of pharmaceutical macrobiotics called "forging external elixirs"[24] whereas Qi Gong exercises said to "refine vital energy" are an internal process of macrobiotics, often called "the inner elixir."[25] The way to ensure a strong constitution lies in "exhaling the stale and taking in the fresh," breathing into the lower abdomen where lies the "elixir field," which will then help to preserve one's vital energy and youthful vigour. An anonymous Chinese poet of the second century A.D. wrote: "Seeking by food to obtain Immortality/Many have been the dupe of strange drugs," pointing out the harm in taking medical pellets or powder, and that only by physical training will one achieve longevity. A vivid picture of ancient Qi Gong exercises can be found in the *Dao Yin Chart*,[26] a painting on silk of the second century B.C. discovered in Han Dynasty Tomb No.3 at Mawangdui in Changsha, Hunan Province. Taoists of the Wei and Jin dynasties (A.D. 220-420) further realized that both liquor and medicine had their demerits and that only sinew-transforming and "refining one's vital energy" was really beneficial to health. These exercises have since constituted an important facet of our national heritage of medical sciences and sports.

The Sinew-Transforming Exercises and the Frolics of Five Animals used to be antedated, erroneously of course, to the times of the legendary Yellow Emperor. The attribution shows no more than the fact that the value of exercises in relation to health had already been observed by the ancients. The Yellow Emperor is believed to have lived in the Stone Age, when pins and needles were made of flint. That is why the first two Chinese equivalents[27] of the word "needle" bear a radical meaning "stone"[28] rather than "metal."[29] The fact that the character "needle"[30] used in the *Classics of Internal Medicine* bears a radical meaning "metal" indicates that the book could not of course have come from the pen of anybody living as early as the times of the Yellow Emperor. However, it may be assumed that the *Canon of Great Void*, which was written in verses with seven characters to each line, must have been a work of the Han Dynasty when the Bailiang style (form of classical Chinese poetry with seven characters to each line) matured.

The *Classics of Internal Medicine* recorded in the "Annals of Art," *History of the Han Dynasty*, did not contain "Plain Questions," since ancient bomboo slips carrying these works, it seems, were already lost. Nor is it possible to verify the *ABC of Acupuncture and Moxibustion* by Huangfu Mi. The currently available text was a hand-written copy done in Japan in the third year of the Hitowa reign period, or the third year of the Guangqi period of Emperor Xizong of the Tang Dynasty in China, i.e., A.D. 887. It does seem probable however that the writing of this book began in the Wei or Jin dynasties and was finished in the Sui or Tang dynasties.

As regards the *Canon of Great Void*, a story goes that the eminent calligrapher and essayist of the Eastern Jin Dynasty Wang Xizhi (321-379) had a hobby for raising geese, and once copied by hand the text of it for a Taoist priest in Shanying (now Shaoxing in Zhejiang Province) in return for his very fine geese. Wang's copy bears the date and place of his calligraphic work: "Done in Shanying County on the twenty-fifth day of the fifth moon of the twelfth year of the Yonghe period," which was in the fourth century A.D. This work was incised on a stone tablet together with his famous essay, the "Orchid Pavilion Preface"[31] in Yingshang (in modern Anhui Province), and, judging from the style of the handwriting, seems to have been inscribed by a Tang Dynasty artist.*

Taoism was held in high esteem in the Tang Dynasty. Its veneration by Empress Wu Zetian, who usurped the throne during the latter half of the seventh century, can be seen from the fact that she designated the years under her reign by such Taoist terms as "Longevity"[32] and "Lasting Perception" (i.e. Good Health and Old Age).[33] When India's Buddhism was introduced into

---

*The copy in my private library is the first rubbing made by an ancient school at Yingshang, originally kept in Haiyuan Pavilion, the private library of a Yang family in Liaocheng (in modern Shandong Province). The Yingshang rubbings are generally regarded as the best in quality of all rubbings of Wang's "Preface."

China, it enjoyed equal respect. We can find traces of the Buddhist and Taoist beliefs blending with each other in Chinese society, for instance some similarities between the intuitional concept of the Chan sect of Buddhism and the Taoist preachings of peace, quiet and inaction, or between India's *yoga* exercises and China's Qi Gong exercises. They were the results of the mutual adoption of ideas between the two cultures following the establishment of the sea route through the South Sea.

Theravada Buddhism (Lesser Vehicle) was the earliest doctrine to be propagated, emphasizing vigorous standards of discipline and asceticism. Mahayana Buddhism (Greater Vehicle), on the other hand, was a slightly later development, absorbing certain Brahmanic concepts and not always so vigorous in its demands. After its introduction into China, the Chan or Intuitional school, which is one of the Sunya sects of Buddhism, gained a strong hold among the educated Chinese. As a result of its need to adapt to the Chinese environment, subsequent Chan masters enriched their philosophy of "enlightenment" and non-attachment to material objects, stressing its more practical aspects and giving it a much greater appeal to the Chinese mind. Legend has it that the first patriarch of the Chan school in China was a Dharma[34] from India. Many bizarre stories about him gained currency at the Shaolin Monastery at Songshan (in modern Henan Province) and were passed on to society at large. Needless to say, all of them have to be thoroughly examined to ascertain whether they be fact or fiction.

In the late fifth and early sixth centuries, Buddhism

was held in high esteem by the Liang Dynasty in southern China and the Wei Dynasty in northern China. Indian Buddhist priests began to come to China in increasing numbers. A rough count in the Tang Dynasty showed that up till then as many as thirty Indian Buddhist priests by the name of Dharma had arrived in China. The word Dharma, or Bodhidharma,[35] means "Buddhist law." It was transliterated as Tanmo[36] in the Chinese language in the Three Kingdoms Period (A.D. 220-265) and the Western Jin Dynasty (A.D. 265-316), this name being shortened to Tan[37] in the Eastern Jin Dynasty (A.D. 317-420). It was not until the Northern Qi Dynasty (A.D. 550-577) that Dharma began to be transliterated into Damo,[38] as in the case of Dharmabodhi[39] (meaning "awakening to Buddhist law") who translated Buddhist sutras at Beicheng (in modern Henan Province) in A.D. 550 and Dharmaruci[40] (meaning "awakening to the fundamentals of Buddhism") who translated the twenty-volume *Brahmanic Astrology* in A.D. 566-571.

As for the Shaolin Monastery, a famous Buddhist establishment in China, its construction began in the nineteenth year of the Taihe period in the Northern Wei Dynasty (A.D. 495), when an Indian monk named Bhadra[41] became the first to open up Songshan. It seems his two disciples, Hui Guang and Sheng Chou,[42] were well versed in martial arts. The Shaolin school of martial arts is reported to have started with Sheng Chou and later flourished in the Sui and Tang dynasties.

Dharma of the Chan sect was from southern India. He came to Guangzhou towards the end of the State of

Song in southern China (A.D. 478). He first visited Jianye (now Nanjing), capital of the State of Liang, and gained an audience with Emperor Wu, but the two failed to see eye to eye in matters of philosophy. He then came north across the Yangtze River to Luoyang, capital of the State of Wei, taking abode at the Shaolin Monastery. He is said to have then sat for nine years facing a wall deep in meditation, after which he passed on the Chan doctrine to Hui Ke[43] which, owing to the sect's traditional dislike of textual authority, was handed down orally ever since. Dharma once said he had lived more than 150 years and had spent about 58 years in China, which means that he must have been a centenarian when he came to China. This and such stories about his crossing the Yangtze on a reed, about his facing a wall for nine years running and his successor Hui Ke seeking to meet him by waiting long in the snow and even cutting off his own arm to show his sincerity are all open to doubt for their obvious exaggeration and lack of common sense.

However Dharma was a highly influential monk of the Chan sect after all. He was idolized and frequently made a subject of paintings and sculptures by many men of letters and artists concerned with Chan in both China and Japan. He was also taken to be the founder of the Shaolin school of pugilism. A verified record shows that he arrived at the Shaolin Monastery in A.D 527 and died in A.D. 536. It is probably in these nine years that he is said to have sat before a wall absorbed in contemplation and preached the Chan doctrine. But silent meditation seemed to contradict with his supposed active boxing coaching and does not tally with his general conduct. The question remains to be a subject of research as to who among the many Indian Buddhist monks named Dharma, if any, was the said pugilist coach.

Qi Gong is different from *yoga,* or *yogacara* in Sanskrit, which has its origins in India's remote past and is a system of health-building exercises combining breath regulation with silent meditation, practised by Hinduist priests. It is generally held that *yoga* was introduced into China in the Southern and Northern Dynasties (420-589). The historical possibility of Qi Gong and *yoga* mutually influencing each other cannot be ruled out, the development of India's Chan Buddhism while in China easily coming to mind. The meditative "lotus" exercise in *yoga* looks very much like the meditative sitting with legs crossed in Qi Gong. In fact, the people of ancient China had the custom of sitting cross-legged on the floor because they considered sitting with one's legs stretched out as disrespectful. Not until the Han Dynasty did a kind of chair[44] originating from non-Han nationalities living in northern and western China, come into use which looked rather like the modern folding chair and on which people would also sit cross-legged. The ancient Indian people also had the custom of sitting on the floor, which has now been maintained by the Indian Buddhists and Brahminists. Indeed in 1945 when I lectured at the International University of Santiniketan in India, my colleagues and I often sat in a circle under mango trees in a nearby forest discussing academic problems.

However *yoga* practitioners can perform many extraordinary feats. It is said that they can lie underground for several hours without suffocation, are immune to attacks by swords and hammers, and can walk on flaming charcoals without suffering burns, amongst many others. The *Old History of the Tang Dynasty*, published in A.D. 945, gives an account of the dances performed by Brahmans at the Chinese imperial court in A.D. 710. It says the dancers could walk on hands, dance on the tips of sharp swords, or lie with their backs on the tips of such swords whilst pipers stood playing on their bellies, after which they suffered no apparent harm.*

These extraordinary skills were said to come from strenuous *yoga* exercises. Qi Gong and *yoga* cannot be just lumped together since each has gone its own way and developed its own distinctive style. Thus the representation of Qi Gong as "Chinese *yoga*" is an incorrect overseas interpretation.

Having come into China and contacted Qi Gong, *yoga* naturally found itself under the influence of Qi Gong. Just as Indian monks introduced their medical arts into China, it can be assumed that Chinese medical arts including Qi Gong were also passed on to India. It is said that in a chart of *yoga* exercises drawn by Indian practitioners in the eighteenth century, seven mystical points were marked out on the human body whose locations are exactly the same as those of such acupuncture points as Niwangong, Shenting, Chonglou,

---

*I recall an Indian friend of mine by the name of Sibruga, who told me in 1944 when he was studying at the Southwest China United Universities in Kunming, Yunnan Province, that as a result of his *yoga* exercises he could lie in a bathtub and control his breath to pump water into his body through the anus to cleanse his intestines and stomach. This is a peculiar way of medical treatment.

Jianggong, Qihai, etc., all of which are distributed along the Anterior and Posterior Midline Channels according to the "channels and collaterals" theory of traditional Chinese medicine. This can be regarded as some of the best evidence of Chinese Qi Gong masters "presenting a plum in return for a peach" in their interchange with Indian *yoga* practitioners. All in all, Qi Gong and *yoga* are creations respectively of the Chinese and Indian civilizations, but they do share one and the same purpose—to preserve health and prolong life.

In another area, records of connections with India have been found in certain Chinese Tang Dynasty dances, amongst them a "Dance of Dharmaci."[45] In classical times, dancing and martial arts were closely related, many dancing postures and forms being similar to those in the practice of martial arts. In one of the books, *Notes on the Music Ward** written by Cui Lingqin in A.D. 762, mention is made of large musical pieces such as *Prelude to Bearded Monks' Dance*[46] and a robust dance called the *Dance of Dharmaci*. The terms "Bearded Monks," "Southern India," "Brahmans" and "Dharmaci" are obviously related to India and those four dances possibly came from India via the South Sea route. Although no relic is on hand to illustrate the postures of the ancient "Dance of Dharmaci," we can consult, say, the sculptured dancing poses that have survived in the Temple of the Lord of

---

*《教坊记》 (*Jiao Fang Ji*). The Music Ward was an official establishment in charge of court music in ancient China. *Notes on the Music Ward* is an important reference work for studying China's musical, dancing, theatrical and acrobatic arts in the seventh and eighth centuries A.D.

Dance in southern India.

Situated at Chidambaram, a city in southeastern Madras, it is the Great Temple of Shiva, who was revered as the Lord of Dance (Nataraja) in southern India. On the walls of the temple complex are sculptured 108 fundamental poses of the robust dance (Tandava-Laksanam), each of which bears a Sanskrit definition in the *Natya Sastra*, or *The Science of Dancing*, a classic by the Indian sage Bharata Muni of about the fifth century A.D. I once asked Mr. Chang Weizhen,[47] author of this booklet and master of the Sinew-Transforming Exercises, if he could find any similarities between the poses of the Indian robust dance and those of the Sinew-Transforming Exercises. He said some of the robust dance poses were surprisingly similar to those in the Sinew-Transforming Exercises, such as "Lad Worshipping Buddha"[48] and "Opening the Window to Behold the Moor."[49] When I was in Santiniketan in 1946, I saw at the College of Music and Dance there the performance of a *Dance of Bharata* by artists from southern India. Wearing precious stones on the head and brooches and laces on the body, they danced with both hands and feet, moving back and forth continuously in measured steps, accentuated with vivid gestures and eye expressions whilst adding choral singing. It was at once dancing and martial arts, a form which had enjoyed ageless popularity among the southern Indians. Living more than a thousand years from the distant Tang Dynasty, we can only hope to visualize the *Dance of Dharmaci* in the image of the *Dance of Bharata*. China and India are two great nations with different glorious civilizations. They have carried on

13

varied exchanges since the medieval times with voyages over the South Sea facilitating the interchange and mutual enrichment of their civilizations. All the similarities in the style and flavour of their dancing and martial arts are consequences of such cultural interflow between the two countries.

Qi Gong in its long history of development in China has branched out into a variety of schools and styles. The Chang-Style 14-Series Sinew-Transforming Exercises have proved to be of considerable therapeutic value. It is my hope that Mr. Chang will achieve still greater successes in his medical work further propagating and expanding his knowledge for the benefit of the people in China and abroad.

Notes

1. 易筋经
2. 气功
3. 黄帝
4. 《黄帝内经》
5. 《汉书·艺文志》
6. 班固
7. 皇甫谧
8. 《甲乙经》
9. 《铖经》
10. 《素问》
11. 杨上善
12. 《黄帝内经·太素》
13. 王冰
14. 《灵枢》
15. 《九灵》
16. 《隋书·经籍志》
17. 杨惺吾
18. 易髓
19. 导引
20. 五禽戏
21. 《医心方》
22. 《黄庭经》

23. 丹田

24. 外丹

25. 内丹

26.《导引图》

27. 碱、矾

28. 石

29. 金

30. 铖

31.《兰亭序》

32. "长寿"

33. "久视"

34. 达摩

35. 菩提达摩

36. 昙摩

37. 昙

38. 达磨、达摩

39. 达磨菩提

40. 达摩流支

41. 跋陀

42. 慧光、僧稠

43. 慧可

44. 胡床

45. 达摩支

46.《胡僧破》

47. 常维祯

48. "童子拜佛"

49. "推窗望月"

INTRODUCTION

The Sinew-Transforming Exercises are a traditional Chinese therapeutic method of exercise. A regular and progressive practice of the exercises, which effectively combine the spirit (concentration), the body and the "breath" (breathing and internal energy), will help regulate the five viscera,* six entrails** and all the channels and collaterals in the body, achieving the effect of preserving health, strengthening the body, preventing or curing diseases, avoiding premature physical decline and prolonging life.

The Sinew-Transforming Exercises, which used to be handed down from master to pupil, have in their long course of development branched out into many different schools and styles. The present 14 Series have been adapted from a private coaching given by an old monk to the author in his youth. The author has also consulted other popular styles in preparing this book. The newly devised 14 Series is a clear advance on previous styles, being more substantial in content and removing certain inappropriate and superstitious aspects.

---

*The five viscera are the heart, the liver, the spleen, the lungs and the kidneys.

**The six entrails are the gall bladder, the stomach, the small intestine, the large intestine, the urinary bladder and the "three cavities" (the thorax and the upper and lower abdominal cavities).

At two training classes opened in Beijing in 1981 and 1982, the author gave coaching on the 14-Series Sinew-Transforming Exercises to Qi Gong practitioners and medical, sporting and physical culture workers from colleges, hospitals and other grassroots establishments in the capital. These classes were sponsored jointly by the Beijing Qi Gong Research Society, the Beijing Trade Union Council, the Beijing Municipal Public Health Bureau and the Beijing Physical Culture and Sports Commission. Satisfactory results of these classes testified to the reputation long enjoyed by the Sinew-Transforming Exercises and have encouraged the author, a carpenter, to set down his coaching in writing for the benefit of the general public. Now, the 14-Series Sinew-Transforming Exercises are being practised by many people in major city parks in Beijing with the assistance of local coaching centres.

The Sinew-Transforming Exercises as a science are based on the "channels and collaterals" theory of traditional Chinese medicine. According to this theory, there exist large channels and small connecting collaterals covering the whole human body, along which are located hundreds of "sinuses," generally known as acupuncture points. All these channels, collaterals and acu-points are closely related to individual organs in the body in a particular way, and certain exercises of the body or a puncture of one or several selected acu-points will help regulate the vital forces in the internal organs and produce the desired effect of strengthening the constitution and curing diseases.

The 14 Series are commendable for an expert choice of acu-points (17 in all) and a simple and easy style, befitting both men and women, old and young. One can do all the exercises, which are interlinked, from start to finish as a physical and mental tonic, or select a particular exercise or group of exercises consecutively for treating a particular disease or strengthening a particular internal organ. The reader is advised to consult the following 20 exercise patterns and make his or her own choice as befits his or her own physical conditions:

Pattern I. Do Series 7 to cure or alleviate the following diseases and syndromes: Abnormal "heat" in palms, Aching arms and lumbago, Apoplexy, Asthmatic coughing, Distension, Fullness and oppression in chest, Excessive "fire" in lungs, Fidgets, Frequent but scant urination, Swollen and aching pharynx and throat.

Pattern II. Do Series 8 to cure or alleviate the following diseases and syndromes: Constipation, Diarrhea, Gastroenteric troubles, Indigestion.

Pattern III. Do Series 8 – Form 2 to cure or alleviate the following diseases and syndromes: Gasterasthenia, Gastric ulcer, Imbalance of vital forces in spleen and stomach systems, Indigestion.

Pattern IV. Do Series 2 and 3 to cure or alleviate the following diseases and syndromes: Common cold, Dry mouth and tongue, Pain or motor impairment in the shoulder blades and surrounding soft tissues, Tonsillitis, Watery nasal discharge.

Pattern V. Do Series 1 and 9 – Form 1, Series 10 and 12 to cure or alleviate the following diseases and syndromes: Abnormal sweating due to high fever, Cephalalgia, Distension in gastric cavity and stomach,

Flatulence, Mental disorder caused by shock, Pain or impaired movement in feet, Stomatitis, Swollen neck.

Pattern VI. Do Series 2, 4 and 12 to cure or alleviate the following diseases and syndromes: Diarrhea, Edema in lower extremities, Emphysema, Gynaecological diseases, Indigestion, Jaundice, Liver and stomach diseases, Pain or motor impairment in lower extremities.

Pattern VII. Do Series 1, 2 and 7 to cure or alleviate the following diseases and syndromes: Angina pectoris, Dry mouth and pharynx, Heart disease, Insomnia, Numbness in upper extremities, Stiffness and motor impairment in neck, Vertigo caused by cephalalgia.

Pattern VIII. Do Series 3, 5 and 8 – Form 3 to cure or alleviate the following diseases and syndromes: Aching shoulder blades and surrounding soft tissues, Cardiopulmonary disease, Dizziness with tinnitus, Hemiplegia, Pharyngalgia from the common cold, Spasm of cervical spine, Trigeminal neuralgia.

Pattern IX. Do Series 2, 6, 9, 10, 13 and 14 to cure or alleviate the following diseases and syndromes: Apoplexy, Common cold, Cystipathy, Duodenal diseases, Emphysema, Epilepsy, Failing eyesight, Flatulence, Heart disease, Impaired movement, Indigestion, Lumbar pain due to exposure to wind and cold, Menstrual disorder, Nephrosis, Night sweating, Nocturnal emission, Pain in lumbar region and lower extremities, Rheumatic paralysis, Rhinitis, Sciatica, Tracheitis, Tuberculosis, Vertigo, Vomiting.

Pattern X. Do Series 9, 10, 11, 13 and 14 to cure or alleviate the following diseases and syndromes: Abnormal "heat" in centre of soles, Amyotrophy of lower extremities, Asthmatic coughing, Cystitis, Dry pharynx and tongue, Gastroenteric diseases, Gonorrhoea, Hemiplegia, Hypertension, Impotence, Indigestion, Leukorrhoea, Lumbago and back pain, Menstrual irregularity, Nocturnal emission, Oppressive feeling in heart and chest, Pain in heels, Palpitation caused by shock and intrusion of "heat," Short breath, Vertigo, Weakness of lower extremities.

Pattern XI. Do Series 1, 2, 4 and 8 – Form 3, Series 9 and 10 to cure or alleviate the following diseases and syndromes: Abnormal "heat" in palms, Angina pectoris, Cardiopulmonary disease, Gasterasthenia, Gingivitis, Halitosis, Hardness of hearing, Hemiplegia, Hiccups, Mental dullness due to apoplexy, Menstrual extravasation, Pain in arms, Pain in sides of chest, Palpitation and fidgets, Paralysis of upper extremities, Spasm of elbows and wrists, Tinnitus.

Pattern XII. Do Series 1, 4 and 8 – Form 3, Series 9, 10 and 11 to cure or alleviate the following diseases and syndromes: Aching arms, Asthmatic breathing, Cervical spine diseases, Coughs, Ear, eye and mouth diseases, Facial nerve paralysis, Hysteropathy, Inability of elbow or arm to bend, Inability of fingers to hold objects, Numbness and amyotrophy of upper extremities, Palpitation with cephalalgia, Pharyngalgia caused by common cold, Tremorous hands.

Pattern XIII. Do Series 4, 5 and 8 – Form 3, Series 9 – Form 2, Series 11 and 12 to cure or alleviate the following diseases and syndromes: Anxiety, Apoplectic paralysis, Cerebral haemorrhage, Cervical spine, Coarse breathing, Coughing asthma, Facial paralysis with mouth and eyes aslant, Fullness in chest, Gastrosis, Hemiplegia, Hysteria, Hysteritis, Migraine, Nephritis, Ophthalmological diseases, Orchitis, Scrofula, Spasm and pain of cervical spine, Tinnitus and toothache, Trigeminal neuritis, Vertigo, Weakness, numbness and pain in legs and knee joints.

Pattern XIV. Do Series 2, 3, 4, 6 and 8 – Form 3 and Series 9 – Form 2 to cure or alleviate the following diseases and syndromes: Anuria, Arthritis, Asthmatic breathing, Chest, rib and lumbar diseases, Cholecystitis, Enuresis, General paralysis, Hepatitis, Hernia, Hypertension, Insomnia, Jaundice, Lower abdominal pain (gyniatrics), Lumbago due to metrorrhagia, Menstrual irregularity, Motor impairment of four extremities, Nephritis, Orchiditis, Paralysis due to exposure to wind, Pneumonia.

Pattern XV. Do Series 3, 4, 5, 6 and 8 – Form 3, Series 9, 10 and 14 to cure or alleviate the following diseases and syndromes: Asthmatic breathing, Cardialgia, Deficient lactation, Distension and fullness in chest, Facial paralysis, Flatulence, Gastrosis, Gonorrhoea, Hernia, Indigestion, Laryngitis, Lower abdominal mass (gyniatrics), Mammillitis, Mastadenitis, Menstrual irregularity, Miscarriage, Pain and stiffness in neck, Palpitation, Pharyngalgia, Rib pain, Spasms of diaphragm, Stenosis of esophagus, Sterility, Tonsillitis, Tooth disease, Tracheitis.

Pattern XVI. Do Series 1, 2, 4, 6 and 8 – Form 3, Series 9, 10 and 13 to cure or alleviate the following diseases and syndromes: Amenorrhoea, Amyotrophy, Anaemia, Back pain, Cervicodynia, Dry stool and retention of urine, Enuresis, Epilepsy, Eye disease, Hypotension, Impotence, Inability to lie down due to asthmatic breathing, Insomnia, Loss of body fluids,

Neurasthenia, Nose disease, Numbness in lower extremities, Pain in sides of chest, Sciatic and hipbone pains, Spasm of shoulder blades and surrounding soft tissues, Stomatitis, Trigeminal neuralgia, Vertigo.

Pattern XVII. Do Series 4, 5, 6 and 8 – Forms 3, 9, 10 and 11 and Series 14 to cure or alleviate the following diseases and syndromes: Amenorrhoea, Deficient lactation, Haematemesis, Menstrual irregularity, Metrorrhagia, Short breath.

Pattern XVIII. Do Series 3, 4, 6 and 8 – Form 3, Series 9 and 10 to cure or alleviate the following diseases and syndromes: Abdominal distension and fullness, Abnormal bloody or whitish discharge from vagina, Metroptosis, Weak lower back.

Pattern XIX. Do Series 5, 6 and 8 – Form 3, Series 11 and 14 to cure or alleviate the following diseases and syndromes: Eye disease, Insomnia, Laryngalgia, Mental disorder, Somnolence, Tightness of muscles on sides of chest and abdomen.

Pattern XX. Do Series 1, 3, 6 and 9 – Form 1, Series 10, 11 and 12 to cure or alleviate the following diseases and syndromes: Cardialgia, Gastralgia, Intermittent chills and fevers, Pain in chest and its sides.

Now a few suggested guidelines:

1. Exercise every day in the early morning in fresh air and tranquil and serene surroundings.

2. Drink a little warm water before the exercises. Do not sprain, overtwist or overstretch your muscles whilst warming-up. Stop exercises of a different nature. Definitely no physical exertion, fatigue, overeating or alcohol before the exercises.

3. Do the exercises in high spirits, with upright posture, all forms accurate. Proceed slowly and steadily. Do not be nervous or stiff.

4. Be calm, the attention concentrated on what you are doing. Avoid disturbances from the "seven passions."* Breathe as naturally as possible—the first and most essential element in all Qi Gong exercises.

5. Perseverance—the key to your success.

6. Progressive training. Do not be anxious to see quick results. Decide your training load according to your physical attributes and the state of your illness.

Every effort has been made to use easily comprehensible language in this book and only a minimum amount of specialized terms of traditional Chinese medicine has been used with a view to augmenting its practical usefulness to overseas readers.

The author wishes to express his thanks to Professor Chang Renxia for his "Preface," which offers an authoritative examination of the historical origins of the Sinew-Transforming Exercises, and Mr. Hong Yunxi, a scholar, who has taken the trouble to revise the Chinese text and translate it into English.

1988, Beijing

Chang Weizhen

---

*The "seven passions" are joy, anger, worry, obsession, sorrow, fear and shock.

14-SERIES
SINEW-TRANSFORMING
EXERCISES

Warming-Up

1. Knee movement: Stand erect, bend forward at waist, apply palms to both knee-caps and turn knee-joints slowly clockwise and counterclockwise eight times each. (Diagrams 1-5)

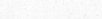

1

2

3

4

5

25

6

7

8

2. Waist movement: Stand with arms akimbo and turn waist slowly clockwise and counterclockwise eight times each. (Diagrams 6-8)

Beginning Form

1. Stand erect, feet placed together, arms hanging down along sides of body, neck straight, chin tucked in and eyes looking ahead. Relax chest and abdomen muscles. Breathe naturally and concentrate your attention. (Diagram 9)

2. Left foot moves half a step sidewise, feet apart at shoulder width. Bend elbows, turn hands into fists and place them under ribs. (Diagrams 10-11)

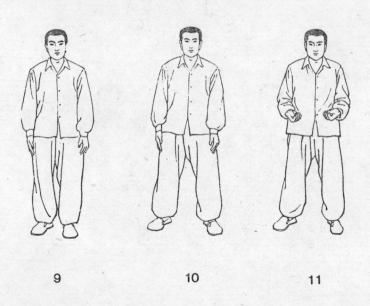

9   10   11

Series 1 – Form 1
Caressing Ball in Horseman's Stance

1. Keep upper torso straight, bend knees forward and squat down to form horse stance, knees right above

12

13

14

toes, lower legs erect. Open fists so palms face upward and extend them forward with force. (Diagram 12)

2. Keep arms straight at shoulder level before you and turn palms so they face floor. Pass palms slowly like paddles by sides of body and to rear till they reach a place slightly higher than hips, palms now facing back. (Diagrams 13-14)

3. Withdraw arms to sides of body, palms facing upwards and fingers pointing towards body. Push hands upward slowly but forcefully as if lifting a weight, until they are slightly above head. (Diagram 15)

4. Maintain horse stance and keep back straight, head erect and eyes looking straight forward. Turn right palm and bend right elbow inward towards face, palm at brow height and facing downward. Meanwhile, bend left elbow in an arc, until left palm is level with

15   16

navel and faces upward. Now palms face each other vertically like holding a ball. (Diagram 16)

5. Set waist, shoulders, elbows, wrists and hips in successive swaying motion from side to side eight times. Meanwhile, hands repeatedly swap positions, describing ovals both vertically and sidewise before chest and abdomen, hands always the same distance apart, palms always facing each other, as if caressing a ball. (Diagrams 17-21)

Series 1 – Form 2
Arms Stretching in T-Step

6. Proceed from last pose. Keep left foot and right heel on floor while effecting 90° inward turn of right foot to form T-Step with left foot. Keep right leg

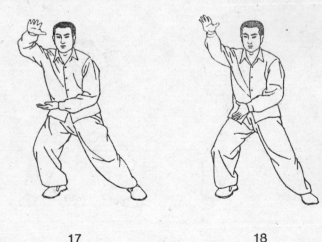

17   18

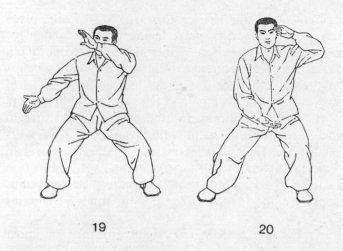

19   20

21

straight and bend left leg forward. Meanwhile, place left palm under ribs, palm facing upward, and place right palm before chest at shoulder level, palm facing floor. Then upper body turns 90° to left, leading palms past each other before chest by pushing left arm forward with force, palm facing ahead and fingers upright, and at the same time pushing right arm to the rear forcefully, palm facing backward and fingers pointing to floor. Now arms are at shoulder level in opposite directions and torso straight, eyes in direction of left fingers in the front. Alternately stretch palms backward and forward like this four times. (Diagrams 22-25)

7. Execute a slow 180° rightward turn of upper torso until right arm is in front and left arm in rear,

22   23

24   25

26   27

both at shoulder level. Meanwhile, make a slow 180° turn of both wrist joints with force so that right palm faces forward, fingers upright, and left palm faces rear, fingers pointing downward. Eyes look to front in direction of right hand. (Diagrams 26-27)

8. Repeat Movement 7 on opposite sides: Make a slow 180° leftward turn of upper torso until left arm is in front and right arm in rear, both at shoulder level. Meanwhile, make a slow 180° turn of both wrist joints with force so that left palm faces forward, fingers upright, and right palm faces rear, fingers pointing downward. Eyes look to front in direction of left hand.

Do Movements 7-8 four times.

Note: In executing these movements, turn feet accordingly when you turn upper torso. Keep the leg before you bent and the one behind you straight. Toes of back foot point to centre of heel of front foot so that the two feet form T-Step.

Series 1 – Form 3
Horseman's Stance

9. Proceed from last pose. Make a 90° left turn of upper torso, eyes looking forward, toes pointing to front, feet at shoulder width. Squat down so that shins form right angles with thighs and feet. Do not protrude knees beyond toes. Meanwhile, swing arms back and then place palms closely together before chest, each facing the other, fingers pointing upward. Turn right palm so it faces floor. Withdraw left palm to under left ribs, palm up, and then thrust it forward. Meanwhile, pull right palm forcefully back, so palms pass by each other before chest. Withdraw right palm to under right ribs, palm up, and then thrust it forward. Meanwhile,

pull left palm forecefully back, so palms pass by each other before chest. Thus hands pass back and forth eight times. (Diagrams 28-31)

28

29

30

31

Series 1 – Form 4
Squatting and Lifting

10. Stand erect. Bring hands to sides of body. Then bend arms upward to form arcs, hands passing by forehead. Press both hands with force from forehead down to ribs, backs of hands facing each other and fingers pointing to floor. (Diagrams 32-34)

11. Thrust hands parallel down past ribs and legs till they reach top of the feet. At the same time, sink down to form sitting position, with back straight, eyes looking forward, knees not protruding over toes and shins at right angles with feet. (Diagram 35)

12. Turn palms so they face floor. Fingers of each hand describe a small circle horizontally and outward without changing position of wrist. Curve fingers of

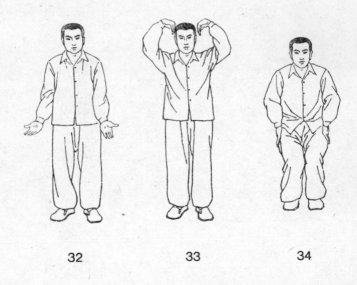

32   33   34

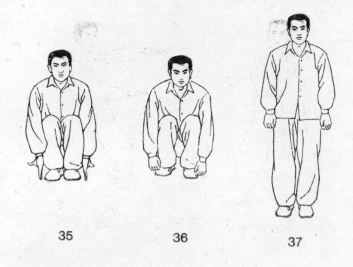

35   36   37

both hands as if lifting an object, move hands upward with force along sides of legs and stretch yourself up into standing position. (Diagrams 36-37)

13. Raise palms from sides of body to ears. Then repeat Movements 10-12.

Do Movements 10-13 four times.

14. Withdraw hands to under ribs and turn palms into fists to resume Beginning Form.

Series 2 – Form 1
Cloud Hands

1. Move right leg sidewise, feet at shoulder width, and stand erect.

2. Stretch arms straight before you, palms facing each other, left palm in slightly lower left position and right palm in slightly upper right position. Then move

38

39

40

41   42

straight arms to left side of body and describe a circle
by moving them rightward to forehead, further to front
and then back to left side of body till they reach left
rear. Turn upper torso leftward accordingly while
keeping it erect and feet motionless. Now right palm is
in slightly lower right position and left arm in slightly
upper left position, palms facing each other behind
you. (Diagrams 38-42)

3. Repeat Movement 2 on opposite sides.

4. Move arms leftward to front of body, up to
forehead, next to right front, and then to left side of
body till they reach lower left rear. Turn upper torso
leftward accordingly. Now the head is turned upside
down and eyes are looking to the rear and upward at
hands.

Then straighten your back, raise your head and
accordingly move straight arms to a higher level while

39

43

44

45

46

47   48

keeping head and body facing the rear and feet motionless. (Diagrams 43-46)

5. Move arms to right rear and then to lower left front, right palm below left palm, palms facing each other. Arms describe a circle overhead and then thrust to left side of body till they reach lower left rear, both palms facing upward. Upper torso is now bent forward, head upside down, eyes looking backward to both hands. While keeping feet motionless, upper torso straight and arms in original position, raise head, straighten your back and turn upper torso backward, palms facing floor. (Diagrams 47-48)

Do Movements 2-5 four times.

Series 2 – Form 2
Waist Turning and Palms Thrusting

6. Continue from above posture. Make a big rightward swing of arms till both hands are overhead,

throwing back your head, and eyes looking at hands when the latter describe a large circle from top of head down to knee-joint. (Diagrams 49-51)

49

50

51

52

Repeat Movement 6 four times.

7. Turn palms so they face floor. Turn upper torso leftward and accordingly effect a 180° turn of shoulders, eyes looking to rear. Meanwhile, arms extend straight and move together from right shoulder to under left ribs and forcefully down to left rear, while keeping fingers together, back straight and feet motionless. Then withdraw hands to left shoulder level, palms still facing floor, while turning upper torso rightward, eyes looking to front. (Diagram 52)

8. Repeat Movement 7 on opposite sides: Turn palms so they face floor. Turn upper torso rightward and accordingly effect 180° turn of shoulders, eyes looking to rear. Meanwhile, arms extend straight and move together from left shoulder to under right ribs and forcefully down to right rear, while keeping fingers together, back straight and feet motionless. Then withdraw hands to right shoulder level, palms still facing floor, while turning upper torso leftward, eyes looking to front.

Do Movements 7-8 four times.

Series 2 – Form 3
Palms Thrusting in T-Step

9. Effect a 90° turn of upper torso to left and move right foot a step forward, right leg slightly bent and left leg straight. Palms each describe a small arc sidewise from under armpit. Then right palm moves in big arc from right side of body to front, thumb pointing to floor and palm facing rightward. Left palm moves in small arc from left side of body to front, fingers pointing upward, till the part of left hand between thumb and index finger is pressed against right elbow

53

54

55

56

joint, palm facing ahead. (Diagrams 53-56)

10. Turn arms inside out, palms facing upward. Withdraw hands to under ribs. Right leg moves a step backward, followed by a rightward aboutface. Turn right foot accordingly, toes pointing to front. Then move right leg a step forward and keep it straight, left leg bent forward slightly. (Diagrams 57-59)

11. Repeat Movements 9-10 on opposite sides: Palms each describe small arc sidewise from under armpit. Then left palm moves in big arc from left side of body to front, thumb pointing to floor and palm facing leftward. Right palm moves in small arc from right side of body to front, fingers pointing upward, till the part of right hand between thumb and index finger is pressed against left elbow joint, palm facing ahead.

Turn arms inside out, palms facing upward. Withdraw hands to under ribs. Left leg moves a step backward, followed by a leftward aboutface. Turn left foot accordingly, toes pointing to front. Then move left leg a step forward and keep it straight, right leg bent forward slightly.

Series 2 – Form 4
Palms Pushing in T-Step

12. Left foot returns to original position. Make a 90° leftward turn of upper torso, eyes looking ahead. Stretch out arms at shoulder level, palms facing upward. Bend arms and withdraw palms to chest. Turn palms into crossed fists, left fist placed between chest and right fist. (Diagram 60)

13. Make a 90° leftward turn of upper torso. Turn feet accordingly to form T-Step, left toes pointing to right side and right toes pointing to front. Meanwhile,

57

58

59

60

turn crossed fists outward. Stretch right arm to front, palm facing forward, fingers pointing upward, and stretch left arm to rear, palm facing backward, fingers pointing to floor. Both arms are at shoulder level. Turn upper torso leftward, head and shoulders turning accordingly, eyes looking at fingertips of left hand in rear. (Diagrams 61-62)

14. Repeat Movements 12-13 on opposite sides: Right foot returns to original position. Make a 90° rightward turn of upper torso, eyes looking ahead. Stretch out arms at shoulder level, palms facing upward. Bend arms and withdraw palms to chest. Turn palms into crossed fists, right fist placed between chest and left fist.

Make a 90° rightward turn of upper torso. Turn feet accordingly to form T-Step, right toes pointing to left side and left toes pointing to front. Meanwhile, turn

61   62

63

64

65

66

crossed fists outward. Stretch left arm to front, palm facing forward, fingers pointing upward, and stretch right arm to rear, palm facing backward, fingers pointing to floor. Both arms are at shoulder level. Turn upper torso rightward, head and shoulders turning accordingly, eyes looking at fingertips of right hand in rear. (Diagrams 63-66)

15. Turn back upper torso, change palms into fists and withdraw fists to under ribs to resume Beginning Form.

Series 3
Pulling and Pushing in Attacking Step

1. Left foot moves a big step to the side, feet more than shoulder width apart, torso tilting to right. Keep left leg straight and bend right leg, with body weight centred on right leg, thus forming Bow Step. Left fist rises to left temple, palm facing leftward. Push it downward along left chest and ribs. Meanwhile, push right fist downward along right chest and ribs. After passing by ribs, both fists turn into palms facing upward, fingers pointing to left front. Push palms further downward along both sides of left leg. Palms join together after passing by left knee-joint and push further downward along left shin till they reach left foot, palms now facing upward and fingers pointing ahead. Meanwhile, bend left leg forward, turn left foot inward slightly, stretch right leg straight and bend upper torso forward accordingly to shift body weight to left leg and form Attacking Step. Press left knee-joint against transverse colon above navel. (Diagrams 67-70)

2. Bend elbows, raise arms and pull palms directly to face, upper torso leaning backward slightly. With-

67

68

69

70

71

72

73

draw palms from face to chest while shifting body weight back to right leg to form Bow Step. Turn palms so they face outward. Keep left elbow above right one. Move waist and elbows in circles twice, first on the left, then on the right. Push palms downward along left ribs and left leg with force, fingers of two hands pointing at each other. Shift body weight to left leg, then pull palms upward along right side of body and left leg, till they reach head. (Diagrams 71-73)

3. Repeat Movements 1-2 on opposite sides: Right foot moves a big step to the side, feet more than shoulder width apart, torso tilting to left. Keep right leg straight and bend left leg, with body weight centred on left leg, thus forming Bow Step. Right fist rises to right temple, palm facing rightward. Push it downward along right chest and ribs. Meanwhile, push left fist downward along left chest and ribs. After passing by ribs, both fists turn into palms facing upward, fingers pointing to rig`it front. Push palms further downward along both sides of right leg. Palms join together after passing by right knee-joint and push further downward along right shin till they reach right foot, palms now facing upward and fingers pointing ahead. Meanwhile, bend right leg forward, turn right foot inward slightly, stretch left leg straight and bend upper torso forward accordingly to shift body weight to right leg and form Attacking Step. Press right knee-joint against transverse colon above navel.

Bend elbows, raise arms and pull palms directly to face, upper torso leaning backward slightly. Withdraw palms from face to chest while shifting body weight back to left leg to form Bow Step. Turn palms so they face outward. Keep right elbow above left one. Move

74

75

76

77

78

79

... and left ... in a ... race, fist in the front, three ... form the chest and elbow, and along with this, and ... the ... form of two hands pointing ... and ... fist ... turn up, then raise ... draw ... left ... and ...

... fixes ... to a horse-stance ...

80

... nail ... with the raised arm ...

In full ... move ... that ... to ...
form ... a ... form the ... side to ... and ...
... on the ... stretch it up ... and ...

81

82

waist and elbows in circles twice, first on the right, then on the left. Push palms downward along right ribs and right leg with force, fingers of two hands pointing at each other. Shift body weight to right leg, then pull palms upward along left side of body and right leg, till they reach head. (Diagrams 74-81)

4. Withdraw arms and legs to resume Beginning Form. (Diagram 82)

Series 4
Palms Pushing in Crossed Step

1. Left foot moves to right rear to form Crossed Step. Make a 180° leftward turn of body on toes of both feet. Meanwhile, arch left arm and raise it to brow

83

84

85   86

level, palm facing ahead. Bend right arm, palm upright
and facing leftward, and push it forward with force
from under left forearm. Withdraw left foot and both
arms to resume Beginning Form. (Diagrams 82-86)

2. Repeat Movement 1 on opposite sides: Right
foot moves to left rear to form Crossed Step. Make a
180° rightward turn of body on toes of both feet.
Meanwhile, arch right arm and raise it to brow level,
palm facing ahead. Bend left arm, palm upright and
facing rightward, and push it forward with force from
under right forearm. Withdraw right foot and both
arms to resume Beginning Form. (Diagrams 87-90)

Do Movements 1-2 four times.

87

88

89

90

Series 5
Wild Goose Shooting Stance

1. Move left leg to right rear and bend it down, upper torso tilting to left, to strike Half-Sitting Pose with Crossed Step. Raise fists to chest. Place left fist on upper left chest and turn right fist both rightward and outward, the part of hand between thumb and index finger facing rightward. Raise right fist to top of head and then push it further upward with force, eyes following movement of right fist. Withdraw fists and legs to resume Beginning Form. (Diagrams 91-98)

2. Repeat Movement 1 on opposite sides: Move right leg to left rear and bend it down, upper torso tilting to right, to strike Half-Sitting Pose with Crossed

91

92

93

94

95

96

97

98

99

100

101

102

Step. Raise fists to chest. Place right fist on upper right chest and turn left fist both leftward and outward, the part of hand between thumb and index finger facing leftward. Raise left fist to top of head and then push it further upward with force, eyes following movement of left fist. Withdraw fists and legs to resume Beginning Form. (Diagrams 99-102)

Do Movements 1-2 four times.

Series 6 – Form 1
Scanning the Sea

1. Turn fists into palms facing upward. Stretch both arms forward from under ribs and left leg straight out backward with force, keeping instep stiff and straight. Now arms and left leg are at a level while right leg, which supports whole body, remains steady

103   104

105

and straight, with eyes looking to front. Turn palms into fists and withdraw arms and legs to resume Beginning Form. (Diagrams 103-105)

2. Repeat Movement 1 on opposite sides: Turn fists into palms facing upward. Stretch both arms forward from under ribs and right leg straight out backward with force, keeping instep stiff and straight. Now arms and right leg are at a level, while left leg, which supports whole body, remains steady and straight, with eyes looking to front. Turn palms into fists and withdraw arms and legs to resume Beginning Form.

Do Movements 1-2 four times.

Series 6 – Form 2
Monkey Beholds Sky

3. Raise left leg and stretch it forward with force, keeping instep stiff and straight. Meanwhile, turn fists into palms and thrust them upward forcefully along sides of chest and head till they reach upper rear overhead, head and upper torso tilting 60° to rear. Keep

right leg, which now supports whole body, steady and straight. Exert strength in direction of two hands and left foot simultaneously, toes kept straight. Withdraw palms and legs and stand erect to resume Beginning Form. (Diagrams 106-108)

4. Repeat Movement 3 on opposite sides: Raise right leg and stretch it forward with force, keeping in step stiff and straight. Meanwhile, turn fists into palms and thrust them upward forcefully along sides of chest and head till they reach upper rear overhead, head and upper torso tilting 60° to rear. Keep left leg, which now supports whole body, steady and straight. Exert strength in direction of two hands and right foot simultaneously, toes kept straight. Withdraw palms and legs and stand erect to resume Beginning Form.

Do Movements 3-4 twice.

106   107   108

Series 7 – Form 1
Pushing Up Heavy Load

1. Place feet closely together and stand to attention Turn palms so they face upward and push them upward along sides of body till they reach back of head. Clasp hands at occipital bone, thumbs pointing downward and pressed against Fengchi Acu-Point at back of head (See Charts of Major Acu-Points, Appendix I). (Diagram 109)

2. Lift heels from floor, toes pressing down on floor with force. Push clasped hands upward with force till they are overhead. Stretch arms, palms facing upward. At same time forcefully press back down onto floor with heels, exerting strength in direction of hands and feet simultaneously. (Diagrams 110-111)

109   110   111

3. Withdraw feet and arms to resume Beginning Form.

Series 7 – Form 2
Lad Worshipping Buddha

4. Proceed from last stance. Push palms sidewise in opposite directions forcefully and stretch out arms, palms upright and facing sidewise. Move wrists to front to keep them closely together, palms facing forward. Turn wrists outward until fingers of both hands point in towards each other. (Diagrams 112-113)

5. Stretch arms forward at shoulder level, fingers pointing upward, palms facing ahead. Move palms so they face each other, roots of palms joining together. Move fingers of both hands forward down like describing an arc till fingers of left hand pointing to lower left front and those of right hand, lower right front. (Diagram 114)

6. Bend arms and turn palms upward and then inward, fingers pointing to upper chest. Meanwhile, lift heels from floor and press down on floor with toes. (Diagram 115)

7. Set palms against each other and turn them upward and forward, fingers pointing to front. Stretch arms forward forcefully and at the same time drop heels back down to floor. (Diagram 116)

8. Separate palms and stretch arms forward with force, palms facing front, fingers of two hands pointing at each other. (Diagram 117)

9. Move straight arms sidewise in opposite directions at shoulder level, palms facing outward, fingers pointing forward. (Diagram 118)

112

113

114

115

116

117   118

119

120

121

69

122   123

10. Turn wrists to set palms upright, facing side-wise, fingers pointing upward. (Diagram 119)

11. Keep arms at shoulder level and turn palms so they face floor, fingers of two hands pointing sidewise. Meanwhile, exert strength in direction of both palms four times and push out lower abdomen. (Diagram 120)

12. Twist wrists so palms are upright. Withdraw arms to chest in a swing, turn palms into fists and place them under ribs to resume Beginning Form. (Diagrams 121-123)

Series 8 – Form 1
Towering Fist and Palm Thrusting

1. Press left fist against Tianshu Acu-Point on left side of navel (See Charts of Major Acu-Points, Appendix I) and place left elbow in the foremost position.

Raise right fist to tip of nose and thrust it rightward forcefully as if driving a screw. (Diagrams 124-125)

2. Place left fist at left waist, the part of fist between thumb and index finger facing ahead. Raise right fist till right arm is fully extended upward on right side of head, the part of fist between thumb and index finger facing forward, eyes looking to front. (Diagram 126)

3. Turn right fist into palm and bend upper torso downward to left, right palm passing by left side of left shin and thrusting to the rear, eyes looking backward. (Diagrams 127-128)

4. Move left fist downward, left thigh squeezing it against small intestine. (Diagram 129)

5. Raise head and rise up slowly, eyes looking ahead. Move right palm in a circle from left side to right front till it is near midline behind the back. Then move right palm in reverse circle till it is extended before you. Withdraw arms to resume Beginning Form. (Diagrams 130-135)

6. Repeat Movements 1-5 on opposite sides: Press right fist against Tianshu Acu-Point on right side of navel (See Charts of Major Acu-Points, Appendix I) and place right elbow in the foremost position. Raise left fist to tip of nose and thrust it leftward forcefully as if driving a screw.

Place right fist at right waist, the part of fist between thumb and index finger facing ahead. Raise left fist till left arm is fully extended upward on left side of head, the part of fist between thumb and index finger facing forward, eyes looking to front.

Turn left fist into palm and bend upper torso downward to right, left palm passing by right side of right

124   125   126

127   128   129

130

131

132

133

134

135

136

137

138

139

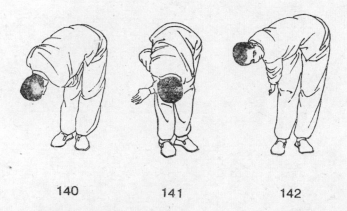

140   141   142

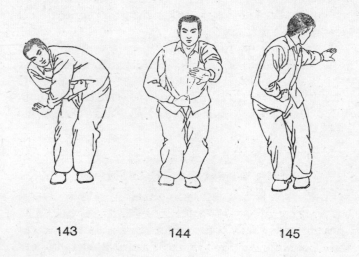

143   144   145

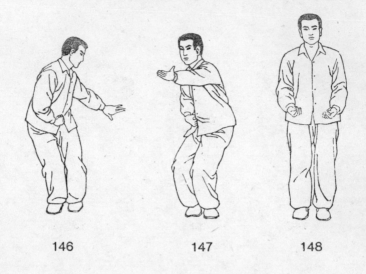

146   147   148

shin and thrusting to rear, eyes looking backward.

Move right fist downward, right thigh squeezing it against small intestine.

Raise head and rise up slowly, eyes looking ahead. Move left palm in a circle from right side to left front till it is near midline behind the back. Then move left palm in reverse circle till it is extended before you. Withdraw arms to resume Beginning Form. (Diagrams 136-148)

Series 8 – Form 2
Waist Movement and Palm Support

7. Press left fist against Qimen Acu-Point under left ribs (See Charts of Major Acu-Points, Appendix I), open right fist into palm and extend it to left side of body, palm facing upward and fingers pointing to left.

Right arm descends in arc from left front to right,
strikes down to the side and up till standing in readiness
overhead, fingers forward. Meanwhile, the upper torso
backward and to the right. Then make half a turn to face of
head, eyes forward, to left front (Diagrams 149, 150, 151).

Keep your arms in a downward pressing to left side,
behind your right shoulder. Right palm facing floor,
legs to walk. Form left side of shoulder, right side,
right knee bending. Transfer body onto the left foot,
right knee downward under the ribs. Turn over the arm to
form the sitting stance (Diagrams 151, 152).

Raise your Microfibres 4-6 cm on guard. Press
from the waist. Quick step forward, clear, push the
left hand of Major Sea leaning. Quickly the right
left the point out and extend it to right side of body.

149

150

151

152

Right arm describes an arc from left front to right front, then to rear and up till right palm reaches overhead, facing upward. Meanwhile, tilt upper torso backward and raise head. Then make leftward turn of head, eyes looking to left front. (Diagrams 149-152)

8. Right palm thrusts downward to lower left side, pulling upper torso erect. Right palm, facing floor, sweeps in an arc from left side of body to right side, right wrist turning so that palm faces upward. Stretch right arm forward from under ribs. Withdraw arms to resume Beginning Form. (Diagrams 153-154)

9. Repeat Movements 7-8 on opposite sides: Press right fist against Qimen Acu-Point under right ribs (See Charts of Major Acu-Points, Appendix I), open left fist into palm and extend it to right side of body,

153   154

155

156

157

158

159

160

161

162

163

palm facing upward and fingers pointing to right. Left arm describes an arc from right front to left front, then to rear and up till left palm reaches overhead, facing upward. Meanwhile, tilt upper torso backward and raise head. Then make rightward turn of head, eyes looking to right front.

Left palm thrusts downward to lower right side, pulling upper torso erect. Left palm, facing floor, sweeps in an arc from right side of body to left side, left wrist turning so that palm faces upward. Stretch left arm forward from under ribs. Withdraw arms to resume Beginning Form. (Diagrams 155-163)

Series 8 – Form 3
Clutching Eagle

10. Right leg moves a big step rightward and toes of two feet turn sidewise in opposite directions. Squat down, shins forming right angles with thighs and feet. Cross fists before chest, left fist placed between chest and right fist, insides of both fists facing chest. Hold back straight and head erect, eyes looking to front. (Diagram 164)

11. Turn the part of right fist between thumb and index finger forward. Raise left fist slowly and turn it outward till the part between thumb and index finger faces leftward. Then thrust it past left shoulder to upper left rear, left arm twisted and eyes looking to front. (Diagrams 165-166)

12. Withdraw left fist to chest and turn the part between thumb and index finger forward. Raise right fist slowly and turn it outward till the part between thumb and index finger faces rightward. Then thrust it past right shoulder to upper right rear, right arm

164   165

166   167

168   169

170   171

172   173

174

twisted and eyes looking to front. (Diagrams 167-169)

 Do Movements 11-12 four times.

 13. Withdraw right fist to position between chest and left fist. Turn fists into palms, right palm facing in, left palm facing out. Thrust left palm further out-

ward to left side till it is stretched straight and upright, eyes looking to front. (Diagrams 170-172)

14. Withdraw left palm to chest, palm facing forward. Thrust right palm further outward to right side till it is stretched straight and upright, eyes looking to front. (Diagram 173)

Do Movements 13-14 four times.

15. Withdraw palms and legs to resume Beginning Form. (Diagram 174)

Series 9 – Form 1
Head and Tail Wagging

1. Squat down to form Horse Stance. Turn fists into open palms and apply roots of both little fingers to Yinlingquan Acu-Points in upper outside parts of both legs (See Charts of Major Acu-Points, Appendix I). (Diagram 175)

175
176

177

178

2. Hold upper torso erect and move it slowly to right side, with body weight shifted to right leg, which is bent at 90° angle. Meanwhile, keep left leg straight. (Diagrams 176-177)

3. Tilt upper torso forward and move it slowly to left side, with body weight shifted to left leg, which is bent at 90° angle. Meanwhile, keep right leg straight. (Diagrams 178-180)

Do Movements 2-3 twice.

4. Withdraw arms and legs to resume Beginning Form.

179   180

Series 9 – Form 2
Behold Moon in T-Step

5. Turn fists into palms facing floor. Make a 90° leftward turn of right foot to form T-Step with left foot. (Diagram 181)

6. Bend right leg slightly, lifting heels while keeping toes on floor. Bend forward left leg, which supports almost whole body. (Diagrams 182-185)

7. Palms swing from before abdomen to left rear and then push with force from under left ribs to upper left rear. Turn waist leftward and at same time raise head, eyes looking to upper rear. Maintain the pose for 30 seconds. Then turn waist back and withdraw palms to resume Beginning Form. (Diagram 186)

8. Turn fists into palms facing floor. Make a 90° rightward turn of left foot to form T-Step with right foot. (Diagram 187)

9. Bend left leg slightly, lifting heels while keeping toes on floor. Bend forward right leg, which supports almost whole body. (Diagram 188)

10. Palms swing from before abdomen to right rear

181

182

183

184

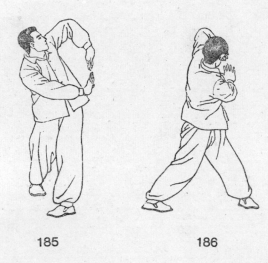

185   186

187   188

89

189   190

and then push with force from under right ribs to upper right rear. Turn waist rightward and at same time raise head, eyes looking to upper rear. Maintain the pose for 30 seconds. Then turn waist back and withdraw palms to resume Beginning Form. (Diagrams 189-190)

Series 10
Swallow Circling Over Nest

1. Proceed from last stance. Bend left leg forward, stretch right leg straight, and shift body weight to left leg to form left Attacking Step. Apply left fist to Shuifen Acu-Point above navel (See Charts of Major Acu-Points, Appendix I) and at same time turn right fist into palm facing upward. Thrust right palm leftward, eyes following palm movement. (Diagrams 191-192)

191

192

2. Right palm describes large circle from left front to right front and then to top of head, palm facing upward all the time. Tilt upper torso backward, bend legs slightly and keep feet motionless, eyes looking to upper rear. (Diagrams 193-198)

193

194

195

196

197

198

199

3. Bend right leg forward, stretch left leg straight, and shift body weight to right leg to form right Attacking Step. Apply right fist to Shuifen Acu-Point above navel (See Charts of Major Acu-Points, Appendix I) and at same time turn left fist into palm facing upward. Thrust left palm rightward, eyes follwing palm movement. (Diagrams 199-200)

200   201

202   203

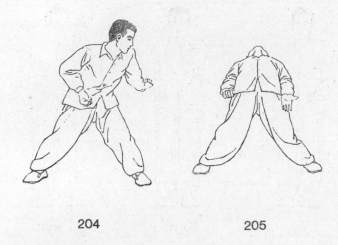

204   205

4. Left palm describes large circle from right front to left front and then to top of head, palm facing upward all the time. Tilt upper torso backward, bend legs slightly and keep feet motionless, eyes looking to upper rear. (Diagrams 201-205)

Do Movements 1-2 twice.

5. Withdraw fists to under ribs to resume Beginning Form.

Series 11
Stand Up to Heaven While Firm on Earth

1. Place feet closely together and hold body erect. While keeping left fist motionless under left ribs, raise right fist to right ear level. (Diagrams 206-207)

2. Move right fist to face, palm facing nose. Turn right fist to right, palm facing rightward. Raise right arm overhead with force, the part of fist between

206   207   208

209   210   211

212

213

214

215

216

217

thumb and index finger facing rightward, eyes looking at right fist. (Diagrams 208-209)

3. Lift right heel from floor and support body with left foot and right toes. Exert strength in direction of right fist and right toes simultaneously eight times. (Diagrams 210-211)

4. Press right heel on floor and withdraw right fist to under ribs to resume Beginning Form. (Diagrams 212-215)

5. Place feet closely together and hold body erect. While keeping right fist motionless under right ribs, raise left fist to left ear level. (Diagrams 216-217)

6. Move left fist to face, palm facing nose. Turn left

218   219   220

221

222

223

224

fist to left, palm facing leftward. Raise left arm overhead with force, the part of fist between thumb and index finger facing leftward, eyes looking at left fist. (Diagrams 218-219)

7. Lift left heel from floor and support body with right foot and left toes. Exert strength in direction of left fist and left toes simultaneously eight times. (Diagrams 220-221)

8. Press left heel on floor and withdraw left fist to under ribs to resume Beginning Form. (Diagrams 222-224)

Do Movements 1-8 twice.

Series 12
Golden Rooster Stands on One Leg

1. Keep right leg straight and lift left thigh before you to form 90° angle with left shin and right leg, which now supports whole body, left hand holding left knee. Raise left shin to keep it straight with left thigh. Meanwhile, stretch out right fist and turn it into palm, which catches left front of left sole firmly. (Diagrams 225-226)

2. Place left hand on hip, straighten back and throw out chest. Turn head leftward to look into left rear. Maintain this pose for one minute. (Diagrams 227-228)

3. Turn back your head and withdraw left leg and both arms to resume Beginning Form.

4. Keep left leg straight and lift right thigh before you to form 90° angle with right shin and left leg, which now supports whole body, right hand holding right knee. Raise right shin to keep it straight with

225   226   227

228   229   230

231   232   233

234   235   236

237   238

right thigh. Meanwhile, stretch out left fist and turn it into palm, which catches right front of right sole firmly. (Diagrams 229-230)

5. Place right hand on hip, straighten back and throw out chest. Turn head rightward to look into right rear. Maintain this pose for one minute. (Diagrams 231-232)

6. Turn back your head and withdraw right leg and both arms to resume Beginning Form. (Diagram 233)

7. While keeping right leg straight on ground, lift left leg before you to form 90° angle with right leg, sole upright. (Diagram 234)

8. Turn fists into palms, which stretch out and both catch Bafeng Acu-Point near big toe of left foot (See Charts of Major Acu-Points, Appendix I). Meanwhile, throw out chest, straighten back and look to front.

Maintain this pose for one minute. (Diagrams 235-236)

9. Withdraw left leg and both arms and turn palms into fists to resume Beginning Form. (Diagrams 237-238)

Series 13
Crouching Tiger

1. Turn fists into palms facing upward and stretch them forward. (Diagram 239)

2. Turn palms into fists and bend elbows to withdraw fists to under lower jaw, palms facing body and the parts of fists between thumb and index finger facing sidewise in opposite directions. (Diagram 240)

3. Twist fists inward, the parts of fists between thumb and index finger facing each other, palms facing chest. Bend forward upper torso, run fists down along

239   240

241 242 243

244 245 246

chest, abdomen and legs and place them on Jiexi Acu-Points of both feet (See Charts of Major Acu-Points, Appendix I). Meanwhile, keep legs and arms straight. (Diagrams 241-242)

4. Lift heels from floor while pressing down on floor with toes of both feet. Meanwhile, raise head and look to front. (Diagram 243)

5. Shrug left and right shoulders forward alternately eight times, bringing waist into swaying motion accordingly. (Diagrams 244-245)

6. Straighten back and withdraw fists to resume Beginning Form. (Diagram 246)

Do Movements 1-6 four times.

Series 14
Breath Regulating and Feet Joggling

1. Move fists from under ribs to small of back, palms facing backward. Press knuckles of both hands against Shenshu Acu-Points and surrounding areas (See Charts of Major Acu-Points, Appendix I). (Diagram 247)·

2. Lift both heels from floor and rub fists upward against Shenshu Acu-Points accordingly; then press heels down on floor, and rub fists downward against Shenshu. (Diagrams 248-249)

Do Movement 2 four times.

3. Withdraw fists to under ribs to resume Beginning Form.

4. Move feet sidewise, shoulder width apart, relax whole body and turn fists into palms facing upward. (Diagrams 250-251)

5. Raise arms to brow level and turn over palms so

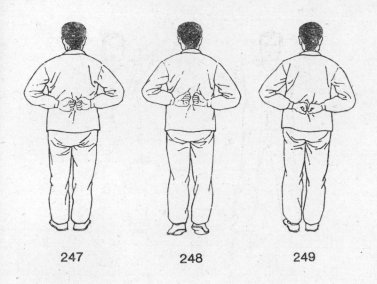

247   248   249

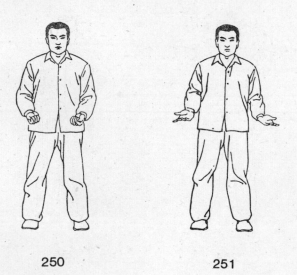

250   251

252

253

254

255

256

257

258

259

they face floor, fingers of both hands pointing at each other. Meanwhile, lift heels from floor. (Diagrams 252-253)

6. Press palms downward from face to chest till they reach abdomen. Meanwhile, press heels down on floor. (Diagrams 254-255)

Do Movements 4-5 four times.

7. Place feet closely together and hands at sides of body to assume Closing Form. (Diagrams 256-259)

Note: Regulate breath throughout the last series.

CHARTS OF MAJOR ACU-POINTS

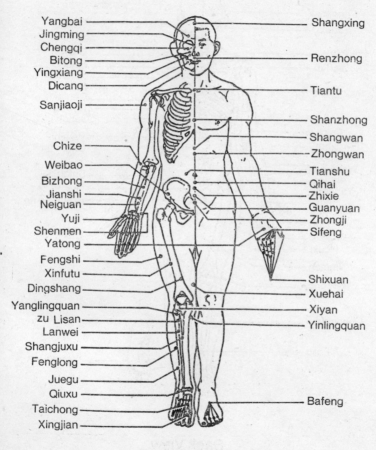

Yangbai	Shangxing
Jingming	
Chengqi	
Bitong	Renzhong
Yingxiang	
Dicang	Tiantu
Sanjiaoji	
	Shanzhong
	Shangwan
Chize	Zhongwan
Weibao	Tianshu
Bizhong	Qihai
Jianshi	Zhixie
Neiguan	Guanyuan
Yuji	Zhongji
Shenmen	Sifeng
Yatong	
Fengshi	
Xinfutu	
Dingshang	Shixuan
Yanglingquan	Xuehai
zu Lisan	Xiyan
Lanwei	Yinlingquan
Shangjuxu	
Fenglong	
Juegu	
Qiuxu	Bafeng
Taichong	
Xingjian	

Front View

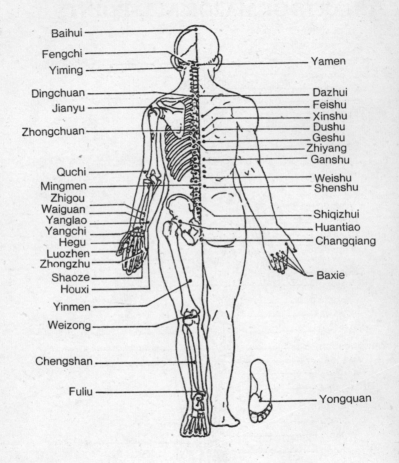

Baihui
Fengchi
Yiming
Dingchuan
Jianyu
Zhongchuan
Quchi
Mingmen
Zhigou
Waiguan
Yanglao
Yangchi
Hegu
Luozhen
Zhongzhu
Shaoze
Houxi
Yinmen
Weizong
Chengshan
Fuliu

Yamen
Dazhui
Feishu
Xinshu
Dushu
Geshu
Zhiyang
Ganshu
Weishu
Shenshu
Shiqizhui
Huantiao
Changqiang
Baxie
Yongquan

Back View

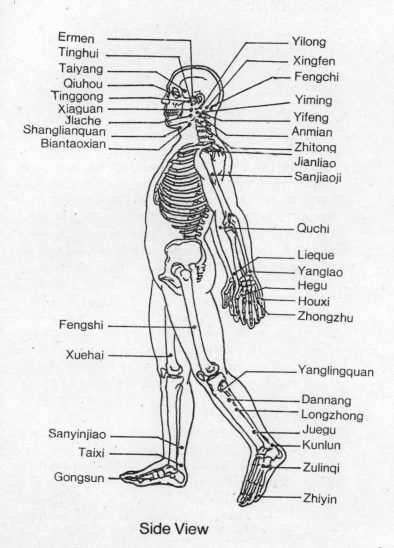

Ermen
Tinghui
Taiyang
Qiuhou
Tinggong
Xiaguan
Jiache
Shanglianquan
Biantaoxian

Yilong
Xingfen
Fengchi
Yiming
Yifeng
Anmian
Zhitong
Jianliao
Sanjiaoji

Quchi

Lieque
Yanglao
Hegu
Houxi
Zhongzhu

Fengshi

Xuehai

Yanglingquan

Dannang
Longzhong
Juegu
Kunlun

Sanyinjiao
Taixi

Gongsun

Zulinqi

Zhiyin

Side View

113

BIOGRAPHICAL NOTES

1. About Chang Weizhen

Chang Weizhen, born 1930, Jixian County, Hebei Province, northern China; carpenter, Member of Council of Beijing Qi Gong Research Society. In his youth learned from old Buddhist monk traditional Chinese medicine including Sinew-Transforming Exercises and Qi Gong Finger-Acupuncture Therapy. Treasures martial and medical arts, persists in Qi Gong and Sinew-Transforming Exercises, offers Qi Gong finger-acupuncture therapy. Coach of two training classes on Sinew-Transforming Exercises in 1981 and 1982 sponsored jointly by Beijing Qi Gong Research Society, Beijing Municipal Public Health Bureau, Beijing Physical Culture and Sports Commission and Beijing Trade Union Council. Chang-Style 14 Series have become popular means of exercises practised by people in major city parks in Beijing.

2. About Chang Renxia

Chang Renxia, art historian on India, Southeast Asia and Japan. Born January 31, 1904, Yingshang County, Anhui Province, China. Graduated from National Central University, Nanjing, 1931; Academy of Literature and Philosophy, Imperial University, Tokyo, 1936. Lecturer, National Central University, Chongqing, 1939-42. Professor, Sichuan Provincial

Teachers College, Chongqing, 1940; National Academy of Fine Arts, Chongqing, 1942; National College of Oriental Studies, Kunming, 1943-45; International University of Santiniketan, India, 1945-47. Now Professor, Central Academy of Fine Arts, Beijing; Director of its library; Research Fellow, Institute of South Asia, Chinese Academy of Social Sciences; Member of Council of Chinese Society of Archaeology; Member of Editorial Staff, *Encyclopedia Sinensis*; Advisor to State Council's Planning Team for Collation and Publication of Old Classics. Author of *A Study of Han Dynasty Paintings*; *The Classical Art of China, The Relationship in Art Between China and India, The Art of the Ajanta Caves, An Art History of India and Southeast Asia, The Relationship in Art Between China and Japan, Random Talks on Oriental Art, Selected Stories from Buddhist Literature, The Silk Road and the Art of Ancient Central Asia*, and four collections of poems.

Traditional Chinese Therapeutic Exercises and Techniques

Atlas of Therapeutic Motion for Treatment and Health
A Guide to Traditional Chinese Massage and Exercise Therapy

Traditional Chinese Therapeutic Exercises
Standing Pole

Chinese Single Broadsword
A Primer of Basic Skills and Performance Routines for Practitioners

14-Series Sinew-Transforming Exercises

Infantile *Tuina* Therapy

Eating Your Way to Health
Dietotherapy in Traditional Chinese Medicine

Keep Fit the Chinese Way

Meridian Qingong

Taiji Qigong
Twenty-Eight Steps

易筋经十四段功法录

常维祯　编著

洪允息　英译

＊

外文出版社出版

（中国北京百万庄路24号）

中国科学院印刷厂印刷

中国国际图书贸易总公司

（中国国际书店）发行

北京　399　信箱

1988年（34开）第一版

（英）

ISBN 7-119-00636-3／R・12（外）

00245

7—E—2109P